December 2005

It's another Quality Book from CGP

This book is for 6-7 year olds.

Whatever subject you're doing it's the same
old story — there are lots of facts and you've just got
to learn them. KS1 English is no different.

Happily this CGP book gives you all that important
information as clearly and concisely as possible.

It's also got some daft bits in to try and make the whole
experience at least vaguely entertaining for you.

What CGP is all about

Our sole aim here at CGP is to produce the highest quality
books — carefully written, immaculately presented and
dangerously close to being funny.

Then we work our socks off to get them out to you
— at the cheapest possible prices.

CONTENTS

Published by Coordination Group Publications Ltd.

Contributors:
Simon Cook
Taissa Csáky
Gemma Hallam
Iain Nash

With thanks to Mr Tansley, Mr Nicol and Class 2 at Broughton-in-Furness Primary School.

ISBN   1 84146 183 0

Groovy website: www.cgpbooks.co.uk

Jolly bits of clipart from CorelDRAW

Printed by Elanders Hindson, Newcastle upon Tyne.

Capital Letters

Learn this rule now — put a capital letter at the start of every single sentence.

You always start with a capital letter.

Q1 Put a **tick** by the sentences that start properly.
Put a **cross** by the ones that **don't**.

| ✓ | My house is near a park. |

| X | it's a massive park. |

| ☐ | There's a big playground and a paddling pool. |

| ☐ | my favourite thing to do at the park is rollerblading. |

Names start with capital letters too. So do titles and headings.

Q2 **Fill in** each gap with the correct **capital letter**.
All the letters you need are in the boxes.

t, p

.....he .....resent

w, e
i

.....hen I woke up, it was a bright sunny day. .....ven better than that, it was my birthday. ..... lay in bed wondering what presents I'd get.

l
c, h

.....ast year I got a monster called .....runcher. .....e's a bit of a pain because he eats cars and trees.

Get off to a good start...

Don't forget your capital letters. They're dead important.

Finishing Sentences

A <u>full stop</u> shows you've got to the <u>end</u> of a sentence.

This sentence ends here.

Cheese is squeezy. Ham is clammy.

Q1 Put a **circle** around all the **full stops** in this paragraph.

*Nectar is a sweet liquid found in flowers.
Butterflies and moths eat nectar. Their
mouths are like long straws. They reach
inside the flower and suck up all the nectar.*

Sometimes you need <u>question marks</u> or <u>exclamation marks</u> instead of a full stop.

?

A question ends with
a <u>question mark</u>.

!

Shouting and orders end
with an <u>exclamation mark</u>.

Q2 **Finish off** these sentences. Each one needs a **full stop,**
an **exclamation mark**, or a **question mark**.

"Do you like butterflies ?"

"They're quite pretty..... Why do you ask....."

"Well, there's a huge one sitting on your head....."

"What..... Get it off me now....."

"Don't panic..... Sit still, and I'll move it....."

"Thank you very much....."

<u>Don't just rabbit on...</u>

Finish <u>all</u> your sentences properly.

Using Speech Marks

You have to put <u>speech marks</u> to show where the words people say <u>start</u> and <u>end</u>.

"Hello," said Gary.

What Gary says <u>starts</u> here and <u>ends</u> here.

Q: Use the words from the speech bubbles to finish off the sentences. Remember to put the words in **speech marks**.

Do you want to see my tarantula?

...*"Do you want to see my tarantula?"* Gary asked.

Shall I come round after school?

Abdul said, ...

No need, I've got it here.

Gary replied, ...

What did you say?

.... gasped the bus driver.

Don't worry, it's not very big.

.... Gary said cheerfully.

You mark my words...

Speech marks go around the <u>actual words</u> people say.

Section One — Writing Skills

<u>Paragraphs</u>

You can split your writing into <u>smaller sections</u> which make it much <u>easier to read</u>. These sections are called <u>paragraphs</u>.

Space!

This is a new paragraph. Your paragraphs need to be clear for anyone reading them.
Leave a space at the start of the first line when you begin a new paragraph.

Q1 **How many** paragraphs can you see in each of these books?

a) There are ....5.... paragraphs.

b) There are .... paragraphs.

c) There are .... paragraphs.

d) There are .... paragraph:

Start a new paragraph when you <u>start</u> writing about a <u>new idea</u>.

Q2 Write down the **reason** for each new paragraph in this story — a **new person** or a **new place**.

new <u>person — Ginger</u> ➤➤ → Ginger the baby giraffe was out on the plains. He was really excited. Granny Giraffe was coming to visit.

new .... — .... ➤➤ → Meanwhile Larry the lion was hiding nearby at the edge of the plain. He was waiting for Granny Giraffe too.

new .... — .... ➤➤ → In the Jungle, everything was quiet. Larry strained his ears to listen. Suddenly, he heard footsteps.

Q3 Write a paragraph to **continue** the story above.

Don't forget to leave a <u>space</u>!

....

....

....

....

Break your writing up...
When something <u>changes</u>, start a new paragraph.

Writing a Story

You need a <u>beginning</u>, a <u>middle</u> and an <u>end</u> for all your stories.
The best way to do it is by <u>making a plan</u> before you start.

Q1 Write **your own ideas** in the space left in these story plans.

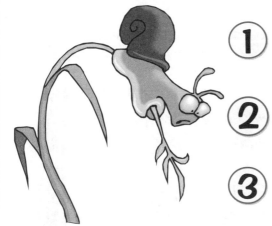

(1) ..The.giant.snail.was.always.hungry.............

.She.ate.all.the.food.in.the.fields..................

(2) The people chased the snail into a cave. She couldn't come out to eat so she got smaller.

(3) When she was tiny, she crept outside.
No one could see her, so she ate what she liked.

(1) I went to visit my uncle. He works at the zoo.

(2) He asked me to help clean the elephant house.
It was smelly but the elephants were amazing.

(3) ....

....

....

(1) Mouldysocks was walking in the wood.
She found a cottage. No one was there and she went in.

(2) ....

....

(3) Mouldysocks heard a noise downstairs. She jumped out of the window and ran away as fast as she could.

Story writing's all about being <u>interesting</u>.
Try using lots of <u>different words</u> to describe things.

Q2 **Describe** in one word how you think Bob is **feeling** in each picture.

....

....

Steer clear of these <u>boring words</u>. They're used <u>all the time</u>.

went   got   said

Q3 Write a **new word** to **replace** each of the green ones.

Jenny *went* to the shops and *got* a comic.

...*cycled*.....   ...*bought*....

I was very angry. "Go away," I *said*.

....

The goat *went* to the top of the mountain.

....

Sarah *got* a big piece of cheese from the cupboard.

....

<u>*Get your story straight...*</u>
Always use the <u>best words</u> you can think of.

Writing a Letter

Letters are really easy to write, as long as you follow the rules.

Q1 Pretend this is a letter from **you** to one of your **friends**.
Use the hints to help you fill in **all the gaps**.

Write <u>your</u>
<u>address</u> here.

....
....
....
....
....

Put today's
<u>date</u> here.

Start with "<u>Dear</u>" and the name
of the person you're writing to.

Dear ....,

    Next Saturday Mum and Dad are
taking me ice-skating. Do you want to
come too?

    Mum says you can stay the night
afterwards.

    Hope you are well.

Write <u>your name</u>
at the bottom.

Love,

....

Q2 Look at these different ways of **finishing off** a letter.
Tick the ones you'd use if you were writing to a **friend**.

☐ Lots of love,
Georgia

☐ Best wishes,
Georgia

☐ All the best,
Georgia

☐ Yours sincerely,
Georgia Blenkins

Oh dear, oh dear, oh dear...

Make sure your letter's got <u>all the right bits and pieces</u>.

Writing Information

Sometimes you have to write a load of <u>facts</u> about a topic.
You can use these <u>three things</u> to <u>help</u> you.

① <u>Main headings</u> ≫→   Frogs & Toads

Frogs and toads look similar but there are
some differences between them.

Frogs
Frogs have long legs, and smooth damp skin.

② <u>Subheadings</u>

Toads

③ <u>Bullet points</u>
* shorter legs
* rough, bumpy skin

Read this short bit of information about <u>frog spawn</u>.

Frog spawn looks like balls of clear jelly with little
black specks in. You can see it in ponds in the spring.
The spawn is really hundreds and hundreds of
frog eggs all stuck together. Every black speck grows
into a tadpole, which then grows into a tiny frog.

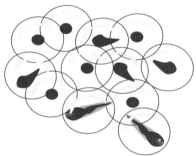

Use the facts to help you <u>answer</u> this question.

Q: Write a **heading** and **two more bullet points** about frog spawn.

....

* *Clear balls of jelly.*

* *You see it in the spring.*

Reed-pulling is a popular
event at the frog Olympics.

Clear as custard...

Set out the facts <u>clearly</u>, that's the secret.

What You Have to Do

Reading comprehension sounds pretty nasty, but <u>don't worry</u>.
All it means is you have to <u>read</u> a short booklet and <u>answer questions</u> about it.

You have to READ something like this.

Read it <u>before</u> you answer the questions.

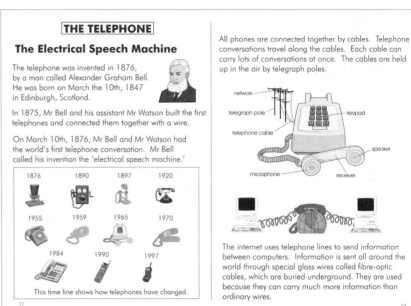

Don't rush — make sure you <u>understand</u> it.

You write your answers in a book that looks like this.

You <u>write</u> your answer in the space or you <u>tick</u> a box.

Read these bits of writing nice and carefully.
Then use the information in the writing to answer the questions.

On March the 10th, 1876, words were sent, and heard using the world's first ever telephone. Alexander Graham Bell called his invention the 'electrical speech machine'.

Q1 What did Alexander Graham Bell call his invention?

The electrical speech machine.

Look — the answer's **there** in the writing.

All phones are connected together by cables. Telephone conversations travel along the cables. Each cable can carry lots of conversations at once. The cables are held up in the air by telegraph poles.

Q2 What are **telegraph poles** used for?

....

The internet uses telephone lines to send information between computers. Information is sent all around the world through special glass wires called fibre-optic cables, which are buried underground. They are used because they can carry much more information than ordinary wires.

Q3 Why are **fibre optic cables** better than ordinary wires?

☐ they can carry more information   ☐ they're pretty

☐ they're made of glass   ☐ they're much longer

How do you answer these questions..?

Read it carefully, then look for the answers — that's how.

Section Two — Reading Comprehension

Stories

A <u>story</u> can be about something that <u>actually happened</u>...

<u>My Holiday</u>   <u>A Visit to the Dentist</u>

... or something <u>made up</u>.

<u>Cinderella</u>   <u>My friend the Alien</u>

<u>Read this story</u> and answer the <u>questions</u>.

There's Something In The Garden

"What's that?" said Anna, sitting up and turning off the television. "There's something moving at the bottom of the garden. Look! There it is again!"

"There's nothing there!" said Charlie, crossly.

Anna rushed to the window for a closer look, but there was nothing to be seen. "I definitely saw something," she insisted. "I don't believe you, I can't see a thing," said Charlie.

Q1 **Why** didn't Charlie believe Anna?   **Look at what Charlie <u>said last</u>.**

....

....

"Let's go and look then," replied Anna. "It might have been fairies!"

She grabbed a torch, while Charlie put on a coat, grumbling, and they went out into the garden. There was nothing there.

"I told you it was nothing," Charlie sighed, "Fairies don't exist!"

Q2 What did Anna **think** she might have seen?

....

Section Two — Reading Comprehension

Keep reading — just a <u>few</u> more questions to go now.

They trudged back inside, and went to the kitchen to talk to Anna's mum. Mum looked up as they came in, and saw Anna's sad face. "What's the matter?" she asked. Anna explained.

Mum thought for a moment. "Why don't we put out a bowl of fruit and nuts? If there is something there, and it's hungry, it'll come out again."

So that was what they did. Mum left a bowl of fruit and nuts on the lawn. Then they went back inside and watched, waiting…

Q3   What did Mum **leave out** in the garden?

....

A short while later, they heard rustling in the bushes.

"Look!" cried Charlie.

"Shh!" whispered Mum. "It's a badger. You can see the white stripes on its face."
"That's better than any fairy!" said Anna.

"And do you know what?" added Mum, "It probably lives nearby. You'll see it again."

"Brilliant!" said Charlie and Anna together.

Q4   Put these sentences in the **right order** by numbering them from **1** to **4**. The first one has been **done** for you.

_____ Mum left a bowl of fruit and nuts outside.

_____ Anna and Charlie went outside with a torch.

_1_ Anna saw a light outside.

_____ Mum, Charlie and Anna saw a badger.

<u>**Don't go wild, just read the story...**</u>

Remember, the answer is <u>there</u> in the <u>story</u>.

<u>Information</u>

When you have to read <u>information</u> you get a load of <u>facts</u>.

<u>Don't</u> make up the answers <u>by yourself</u>.

You need to <u>read</u> the article and <u>find</u> the facts <u>there</u>.

<u>Read</u> this piece about fossils and <u>answer the questions</u>.

Fossils

Fossils are things preserved in rock from thousands of years ago. They can be the remains of dead plants or animals, or footprints and tracks that have stayed imprinted in the rock.

Maybe it's me?

Q1 What are **fossils**? Tick the correct box.

☐ things you eat

☐ things that live forever

☐ things preserved in rock

☐ things for sale

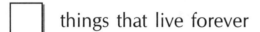

How Fossils Are Made

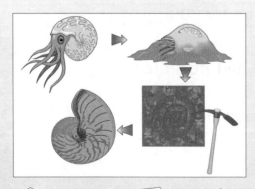

When an animal or plant dies, it usually rots away. But if it falls into soft mud, then it is preserved. Over time, the mud is pushed underground and dries up, tuning into rock. The remains of the animal or plant also sometimes turn into rock, or leave an imprint on the rock around them. The rock that's left is a fossil.

Q2 What **usually happens** to an animal or plant when it dies?

....

Look at the <u>pictures</u> too. They're there to <u>help you</u>.

Fossil Sizes

Fossils come in all shapes and sizes. The biggest complete one ever found was the fossilised skeleton of a dinosaur called *Brachiosaurus*. It measured 23m from the tip of its tail to end of its nose, and 13m in height — that's bigger than most houses!
        Some fossilised bones have been found that could come from dinosaurs as long as 46m. That's as long as FIVE buses parked end to end! We can't be sure, though, because we don't always have the whole skeleton.

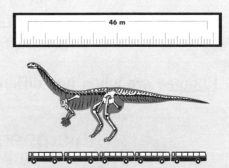

Q3   Which dinosaur left the biggest complete fossil?

....

Q4   How long could the biggest dinosaurs have been?

....

Even things as small as leaves and insects have been found as fossils.
As far as dinosaur fossils are concerned, the smallest complete one is a dinosaur called *Compsognathus*. It was less than 1m long and probably weighed about 2.5 kg, the same weight as a frozen chicken.

Q5   How was *Compsognathus* like a frozen chicken?

....

D'you think 'e saurus...

Always LOOK for the <u>facts</u> in the <u>writing</u>.

Poems

Poems are <u>short</u> bits of writing that often use <u>word patterns</u> or <u>rhymes</u>.

Look out for these <u>three things</u> in every poem you read:

- what is the poem about?
- what describing words are used?
- do any words rhyme?

<u>Rhymes</u> are when two different words <u>sound like</u> each other — like <u>rat</u> and <u>cat</u>.

Read this poem and <u>answer</u> the questions.

The Prince of the Air

He lives in my garden
And sings through the **year** —
His song always happy,
His voice always **clear**.

He's there in the summer
He's there in the spring.
I wake up each morning
When I hear him sing.

He's seen lots of winters,
Some good and some bad,
But still he keeps singing —
He never seems sad.

His breast is bright red,
There is brown on his wings,
And I always feel better
Whenever he sings.

It makes me so happy
To know that he's there.
My friend, the robin,
The Prince of the Air.

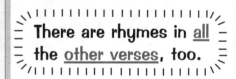

These two words <u>rhyme</u>.

There are rhymes in <u>all</u> the <u>other verses</u>, too.

Look — the poet has written about his feelings.

Watch out for these questions. They're a bit more tricky.

Q1 **Who** is the Prince of the Air?

....

Q2 What does the poem tell you about the 'Prince of the Air'?
Tick the box that **describes** him.

I think I'm rather handsome...

☐ ugly ☐ sad

☐ naughty ☐ happy

Q3 Look at the words at the **end of each line** of the poem.
Write down the words that **rhyme**. The first one is done for you.

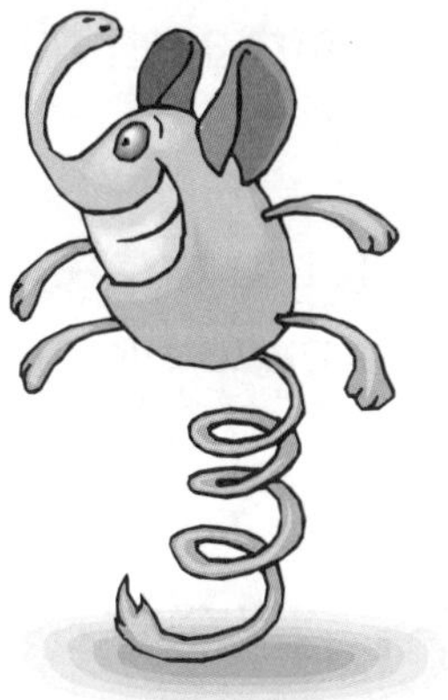

year ....*clear*..........

spring ....

bad ....

wings ....

there ....

Q4 What does the person who wrote the poem
think of the 'Prince of the Air'?

Say what you think here.

☐ that he is a friend ☐ that he is an enemy

☐ that he is a pet ☐ that he is a garden pest

Poetry in motion...
Be careful with questions about <u>what you think</u>.

Section Two — Reading Comprehension

Getting Started

Finding your way around the test booklet is easy-peasy.
The contents page tells you the titles and page numbers of all the bits of writing.

All About Food

Salad 3
A poem about salad.

The Lizard and the Peach..4-5
A story about greed.

What's on the Menu? 6
Facts about the food we eat.

There are three bits of writing in this booklet.

Go to this page to read a poem about salad.

There'll be different kinds of question about each bit of writing.

Q1 Look at the **contents page** above.
Which page would you look at to find out about the food we eat?

....

Q2 What's the title of the **story** about **greed**?

☐ Salad

☐ The Lizard and the Peach

☐ What's on the Menu

Use your loaf...

The contents page tells you what to expect.

Salad

Read the <u>whole poem</u> before you do the questions.

Salad

I'm bored of chips, I'm bored of beans,
Give me plates piled high with greens.

Give me a lettuce on my plate,
Give me celery, it tastes great!

Put some cucumber on the top,
Slice a tomato, chop chop chop.

It's healthy food and fun to crunch,
Please give me salad for my lunch!

Q1　Name **two things** that go into the salad in the poem.

a) ....

b) ....

Q2　Which word **rhymes** with **plate?**

☐ lunch

☐ chop

☐ great

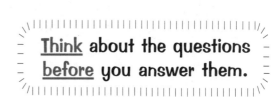

Think about the questions **before** you answer them.

Don't be a wormy apple...

It's as easy as this — <u>read</u>, <u>think</u>, <u>answer</u>.

The Lizard and the Peach

Here's a <u>story</u>. Read it <u>carefully</u> and answer the questions on the <u>next page</u>.

The Lizard and the Peach

One day, a lizard was sitting in the sun and thinking about dinner. "I'm sick of flies," he moaned, "Flies for breakfast, flies for lunch, flies for dinner. All I ever eat is flies. Nothing but horrible crunchy flies. They don't even taste of anything."

The lizard looked up at the peach tree overhead. One huge peach dangled down from a low branch.

"That peach looks delicious," thought the lizard, licking his dry lips with his long tongue. He imagined how sweet and soft and juicy the peach would be. Nibbling at the fresh peach would be a hundred times better than sucking the tasteless innards out of a housefly.

It was time for action. The lizard scuttled over to the peach tree. He stood under the tree and looked up at the peach. It was hanging very close to the ground. "That peach doesn't look too far away. I bet if I jump, I'll be able to reach it," thought the lizard.

He stepped back and took a run at it. He leapt into the air with his lizard feet spread out to catch hold of the peach. Unfortunately, the peach was a little bit higher than he'd thought. His belly made a slapping sound when it hit the ground.

The lizard dusted himself off and tried again. The same thing happened. He fell flat on his face. After half an hour of jumping, the lizard was completely worn out.

He brushed the dust off his belly and looked up at the peach. "I don't want it now, it must be rotten or something," he said crossly, as he limped off to catch some flies.

Q1 What does the lizard **usually** eat?

....

Q2 **Why** does the lizard want to eat the peach?

> Look at what the lizard thinks about the peach.

☐ because lizards always eat peaches

☐ because the peach would be nicer than flies

☐ because he doesn't like bananas

Q3 Write down **three** words that **describe** the **peaches**.

a) ....

b) ....

c) ....

Q4 **How** does the lizard try to get the peach?

☐ By climbing the tree   ☐ By jumping

Q5 Why do **you think** the lizard says that the peach is **rotten**?

....

....

HINT: Think about how the lizard **felt** when he couldn't get the peach.

Answer the question, pal...

You need to **find** the **right bits** of the story.

What's on the Menu

Read this list of <u>facts</u> about food, then answer the questions underneath. It's just like eating your dinner — <u>don't</u> rush it.

Some Food Facts

Half a million curries are eaten every day in the UK. Chicken tikka masala is the best-selling curry. It was invented in Glasgow.

The most popular pizza toppings in the UK are ham, mushroom, and pepperoni.

Most people eat fish and chips at least once a month. Fish and chips is Britain's most popular takeaway meal.

Q1 **Finish** these sentences with the **correct facts** from above.

In the UK, ... curries are eaten every day.

The most popular takeaway meal in Britain is ....

Q2 **Where** was chicken tikka masala invented?

....

Q3 What are the **three most popular** pizza toppings?

☐ mushroom, ham and pepperoni

☐ baked beans, curry and onion

Food for thought...

<u>Don't rush</u> — work through it all carefully.

Section Three — All About Food

Questions on the Whole Lot

The last part of the test is questions on <u>all</u> the bits of writing in the booklet. You need to think about <u>what kinds</u> of writing you've read.

Q1 Put a **tick** under the **title** of the writing where you read these things.

Decide if you think each thing is a <u>fact</u>, part of the <u>story</u> or part of the <u>poem</u>. Then go back and <u>check</u>.

	Salad	The Lizard and the Peach	What's on the Menu?
Most people eat fish and chips at least once a month.			✓
It was time for action.			
Give me celery, it tastes great!			
His belly made a slapping sound when it hit the ground.			

Q2 How is the lizard in the **story** like the writer of the **poem**?

....

HINT: Think how they both feel about their <u>normal</u> food.

Q3 In which bit of writing would you find a **picture** of a **peach**?

....

Time to chew it over...

Don't forget to look at <u>all</u> of the writing.

Writing a Story

The writing task is <u>totally separate</u> from the reading comprehension test.
You have to write about something you've <u>read in class</u>.

> The story on **page 20** is about a lizard who tries to pick a juicy peach.
> Write a story about someone who **wants special food** and **gets it**.

First of all you need to make a <u>note</u> of your ideas here.
Answer these questions to help you think.

Who is in your story?

....

Write down the <u>names</u> of the people or
animals you're going to put in the story.

Write down **three things** that will happen in your story.

<u>HINT</u>: Think what the story's <u>about</u>.

It's about someone who <u>wants special food</u> and <u>gets it</u>.
Now think of three things that <u>could happen</u> in it.

....

....

....   Don't try to put <u>too</u>
                                                            <u>much</u> in your story.

You also need to think about <u>what kind</u> of special food it is.

What is the special food in your story?

....

You've got to work out how to make the story <u>interesting</u>.
The easy way is to <u>make a list</u> of interesting words you can use.

Write down some **interesting words** to describe the food.

....

....

Think about these things too.

*   How you are going to **start** the story.

    **Start by saying <u>who</u> the <u>main character</u> is
    and <u>what special food</u> he or she wants.**

*   How the people or animals in your story **feel**.

    **Make sure the people or animals in
    the story <u>say</u> what they <u>feel</u>.**

*   How you are going to **end** the story.

    **Find a piece of paper and write your story.
    Remember to <u>use your notes</u> to help you.**

Easy as pie...

Always write <u>notes</u> to help you <u>plan</u> your story.

A Wintry Weekend

Hey, it's a <u>story in two parts</u>. It's all about winter weather.
Be sure to read it properly — there are some <u>questions</u> coming up.

Part 1 — The Rain.

Chris lay in bed and listened to the weather. Rain fell on the window as if someone was throwing handfuls of gravel at his house. He could hear his dog, Candy, barking at the garden gate, which was banging open and shut in the wind. "I'd better take her for a walk," he thought, "even though it's raining."

Chris got up and went downstairs. Candy was dancing around the kitchen like a crazy puppy. "Hang on a minute, Candy," he said, "Settle down, we'll go for our walk when I've had my toast." Candy grabbed her leash, and sat waiting by the front door.

When Chris opened the door, a sudden gust of wind blew a wet, brown leaf into his face. "Yuck!" he exclaimed, pulling the door closed behind him. The wind was blowing the rain almost sideways. The cold raindrops stung Chris's face, and he held his umbrella out in front of him like a shield to protect himself.

They made it to the end of the road. Candy's coat was soaked and her fur stuck to her back. She looked as if she had been shrunk by the rain.

The trees looked sad and bare. Their leaves had been blown off, and were lying in soggy, brown heaps on the pavement. The trees waved their branches in the wind as if they were waving their arms.

Home, Sweet Home

When they got back home, Candy shook the water out of her coat. Water sprayed everywhere. It was like another rainstorm, only this time it was inside the house. Chris wished he'd put some newspaper down. "What a miserable winter's day!" he thought to himself.

Phew — Part 1 was pretty <u>miserable</u>, wasn't it?
See <u>what happens</u> in Part 2. It could be <u>similar</u> or <u>different</u> to Part 1.

Part 2 — The Snow.

As soon as Chris woke up, he thought there was something peculiar going on. It looked unusually light inside his bedroom. It was also very peaceful outside, as if the whole world was fast asleep. Chris checked the time.

He got out of bed, opened the curtains, and gasped. The whole world had gone white. The trees looked like huge marshmallows. Each twig looked like it was wearing a thick white glove. "Better put *my* gloves on today!" he thought.

Chris didn't even stop for breakfast. He couldn't wait to take Candy out. As soon as he opened the door, Candy bounded outside. The snow came right up to her knees. She picked her way through it neatly, as if she was dancing.

Chris picked up a handful of snow. He squeezed it into a ball and threw it. Splat! The snowball exploded in a puff of powder as it smashed beside her. She yelped, happily. He threw another. She jumped up and caught it in her mouth, half of it bursting over her head.

As they played, neighbours came out to see what was happening. Once they'd seen the snow, they rushed back inside to get their coats and scarves. Soon there were almost twenty people having a snowball fight in the street.

Pretty soon, Chris and Candy were both exhausted. They made their way back through the snow, cold but happy. When they got back inside, Candy curled up by the fire straightaway. Chris rested in an armchair. "What a wonderful winter's day!" he thought.

Read both parts of the story...

<u>Don't</u> leave anything out — read the <u>whole lot</u>.

A Wintry Weekend

Get ready for some <u>questions</u> on the story.
Remember to <u>look back</u> at the story to find the answers.

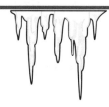

These questions are all about
the <u>first part</u> of the story.

Part 1 — The Rain

Q1   What **two things** could Chris hear as he lay in bed?   (page 26)

....

....

Q2   What stung Chris's face in the story?   Don't guess. Check what it <u>really</u> says.

☐ bees

☐ nettles

☐ cold raindrops

☐ the wind

Q3   Why did Chris hold his umbrella out **in front** of himself?

....

....

Q4   Why did Candy look like she had been **shrunk**?

☐ she was getting further away

☐ a witch was shrinking her

☐ the rain was sticking her fur down

☐ she couldn't swim

Section Four — Frost and Snow

This is where things get <u>harder</u>. Think about these questions <u>before</u> you answer.

These <u>numbers</u> tell you <u>where to look</u>.

Part 2 — The Snow

(page 27)

Q5 Why did the trees look like **marshmallows**?

....

....

Q6 **What** did the twigs look like they were doing?

....

Q7 What do you think is **different** about the end of Part 2?

☐ Chris and Candy are sad   ☐ Chris and Candy are bored

☐ Chris and Candy are happy   ☐ the snow has gone

Q8 Write down three things that happened in **both** parts of the story.

1) ....

2) ....

3) ....

Don't get snowed under...

Watch out for questions on <u>both parts</u> of the story.

Section Four — Frost and Snow

Snow Facts

Go on — you know you can do it. Just <u>read</u> this lot and <u>do</u> the questions. It's better than being stuck out in the cold all day...

Snow Facts

- Snowflakes are made of tiny ice crystals that clump together and freeze into a bigger crystal.

  - The largest snowflake ever found was 21cm by 30cm. It fell in Bratsk, Siberia in 1971.

    - No two snowflakes look the same, but they are all either six-sided shapes or six-pointed stars.

  - More snow falls in Canada and the northern United States than falls at the North Pole.

  - Snowflakes only get to the ground if the air is freezing all the way down from the cloud. Sometimes they melt before they get there, and turn to sleet or rain.

  - It can be snowing on top of a skyscraper but raining at the bottom, because the air is warmer down below.

- Snow can be either dry or wet snow — dry snow forms when it's really cold. It's made up of small, powdery crystals. Wet snow is formed when it's only just freezing. It's made up of large snowflakes and melts very easily — that's why it feels wet.

Q1 What are snowflakes **made** of?

....

I can't tell you often enough — the answers are right there if you look for them.

Q2 **Where** was the largest snowflake found?

....

Q3 **Finish** these sentences, using the **Snow Facts** to help you.

More snow falls in ....

....

Snowflakes only get to the ground ....

....

Q4 How can it **snow** at the top of a skyscraper and **rain** at the bottom?

....

....

....

Q5 What sort of snow is formed when the temperature is only **just freezing**?

☐ wet snow ☐ pink snow

☐ rain or sleet ☐ dry snow

It SNOW joke, you know...
As long as you read carefully, you'll be totally fine.

Frosty Stories

Hurrah — you <u>don't</u> always get long stories to look at.
You could get a couple of <u>short ones</u>, with some facts to help you read them.

Introduction

Many years ago, people didn't know as much about the weather. They made up stories to explain things like frost and snow.

Some of these tales try to explain the beautiful patterns that frost makes on our windows. Other stories try to explain why things freeze, and how the world gets so cold in winter.

Here are two stories people have made up about cold weather.

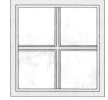

The Snow Queen

This fairy story, written by Hans Christian Andersen, explains why frost patterns appear on windows in the winter. It talks about the Snow Queen who looks through people's windows at night. When the Snow Queen looks through a window, the window freezes in a beautiful pattern that looks like flowers. She steals children and turns their hearts to ice with her deadly icy kisses.

Morozko

The story of Morozko, or Father Frost, comes from Russia. Morozko is a clever, cruel man who freezes everything he touches with his icy grip. In one story, Morozko finds a girl in the woods in the middle of winter. The girl recognises him and is very polite. Instead of freezing her, he gives her fur coats to keep her warm and jewels to reward her.

A greedy woman leaves her own daughter in the woods, expecting that Morozko would give her a fur coat and jewels too. This girl is rude to Morozko, and he becomes so angry that he freezes her solid. The story warns people to respect Morozko and the cold weather he brings, or else they will freeze in the winter.

Careful — <u>don't</u> get the two stories <u>mixed up</u>.

Nice and slowly — that's how to do these questions. <u>Don't</u> rush.

Q1 In **The Snow Queen**, what happens to a window when the Snow Queen looks through it?

....

....

Q2 How does the **Snow Queen** freeze children's hearts?

☐ with an ice spear ☐ with her kisses

☐ with an ice cube ☐ with flowers

Q3 What does **Morozko** do to the girl who is polite to him?

....

....

Eeek! This one's pretty <u>tricky</u>.
Think <u>extra-carefully</u>.

Q4 What do you notice about the **way** winter weather is explained in both **Frosty Stories**?

☐ a person causes the cold weather ☐ it happens by accident

☐ it always happens at Christmas ☐ it comes from Russia

Frost sounds cool to me...

Don't mix the <u>two stories</u> up and you'll be fine and dandy.

Questions on the Whole Lot

<u>Nearly</u> there now. Only this set of questions to go.
Keep your eyes peeled though — they're a bit <u>sneaky</u>.

I'm not sure I can manage a whole one...

<u>Look back</u> over the <u>whole section</u>.

Q1   In what part of the booklet would you find a **story** that **describes** the weather on two wintry days?

☐   ***A Wintry Weekend***   ☐   ***Frosty Stories***

☐   ***Snow Facts***

Q2   In which part would you find two stories that try to **explain** frost?

....

Q3   Fill in the **missing bits** of these sentences.   The sentences could come from <u>anywhere</u> in the section.

Each twig looked like ....

....

....   I thought you said wigs...

She steals children ....

....

Don't forget to check...

Always <u>look back</u> at the section <u>before</u> answering.

Section Four — Frost and Snow

Writing Information

After all that reading about <u>frost and snow</u>, you'd think you deserve a <u>rest</u>. Well, think again. It's <u>your turn</u> to do some writing.

Look at <u>how</u> "Frost and Snow" is <u>set out</u>.

Answer these questions to help you <u>plan</u> your own writing.

Go back to the <u>Snow Facts</u> on P.30.

What have you found out about **snow**?

Think about the <u>kind</u> of thing you found out — like <u>what snow is made of</u>.

....

....

....

....

....

...to make snow, take a large block of ice...

How is the information **set out**? Tick the **two** correct boxes.

☐ using arrows ☐ using boxes

☐ using a heading ☐ using bullet points

<u>Work out how to do it first...</u>

That's the <u>secret</u> with writing <u>information</u>. Don't rush in.

Writing Information

This is more like it. <u>Have a go</u> at this writing task.

Use this page to <u>plan</u> your writing.

All you've got to do is <u>think</u> before you <u>write</u>. Easy, isn't it.

The Weather

Choose **one kind of weather** to write about.
Tick the one you choose.

Wind ☐   Sun ☐   Rain ☐   Your own idea ☐

<u>Don't</u> just choose the first one.
Try to pick one that you know <u>lots about</u>.

Your writing needs to be in **your own words**.
You can look for facts to put in **anywhere** you like.

Start by thinking about:

- what **kind** of facts you want to put in

....

....

....

....

It <u>isn't</u> just about what you <u>write</u> though — you can draw <u>pictures</u> too.

Think about:

- what **pictures** you want to put in

    Try drawing some <u>practice pictures</u> in these boxes.

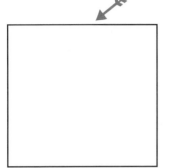 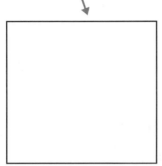 

    Remember — the pictures need to be <u>clear</u> and <u>useful</u>.

You could also <u>split</u> your writing up into <u>sections</u>.
Each section could have a <u>title</u>.

Write down what the **title** of each part will be.

① ....

② ....

③ ....

All ready to go — but <u>don't forget</u> to think about:

- how you will **set out** your writing.

- how you will make it **interesting**.

Get some paper and <u>write</u> your piece.
<u>Use these notes</u> to help you.

<u>*Stick to the facts...*</u>

Stay on top of it. Keep it <u>easy</u> and it'll be easy!

Getting Started

Another test coming up. Another chance to show how <u>totally excellent</u> you are. Do it <u>really well</u> — it's the <u>last one</u> in the book.

Look at the <u>contents</u> and see what it's all about.

Up and Away

Don't spend <u>ages</u> looking at this — just long enough to get the <u>general idea</u>.

If there's an <u>introduction</u>, that'll tell you what to expect too.

Introduction

The balloons you get at parties are great. You can throw them around, or rub them on your head and stick them to the ceiling. On a hot day you can fill them up with water, then take them outside and have water fights.

The pieces of writing in "Up and Away" are all about balloons — the kind you get at parties, and the kind which people use to fly high into the air.

Now you know what sort of things there'll be in the test. Read the <u>poem</u>, the <u>story</u> and the <u>information</u>, then answer the questions. They start on <u>page 44</u>.

Chocks away...
Time to <u>get stuck in</u> to reading.

My Balloon

Read this poem <u>first</u>. Don't race through, just read it a bit at a time.
Read it <u>slowly</u>, and don't turn over till you're sure you've <u>understood</u> it.

My Balloon

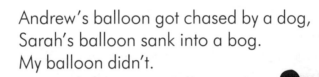

David's balloon got stuck in a tree,
Mary's balloon got dragged out to sea.
My balloon didn't.

Andrew's balloon got chased by a dog,
Sarah's balloon sank into a bog.
My balloon didn't.

Charlie's balloon lost all of its air,
Laura's balloon got caught in her hair.
My balloon didn't.

Anna's balloon fell into a drain,
Ruari's balloon got hooked on a train.
My balloon didn't.

My balloon was much too light,
I shouldn't have held it quite so tight.
BANG!
My balloon burst.

Hold on tight...

That's the <u>poem</u> read. Turn over for the <u>story</u>.

The First Balloon Ride

**So here's the <u>story</u>. It's based on something that <u>really happened</u>.
The first little bit's an <u>introduction</u> to help you understand what's going on.**

The hot-air balloon was invented in France by the Montgolfier brothers. But they weren't the first people to fly in it. In fact, the first people to fly in a balloon weren't even people at all. They were animals — a sheep, a cockerel and a duck. This is a story about that first balloon ride, back in 1783.

The First Balloon Ride

The first thing I knew about it was when two strange men came to speak to the farmer. They were dressed smartly, but they looked worried.

"We need some animals," said one.

"The King himself has ordered it," said the other one. They were both sweating in their fine suits and wigs. These humans wear some silly clothes!

The farmer let the two men borrow a sheep, a cockerel and me. They loaded us into a large box, and after a few minutes bumping up and down, the box was opened.

We were in a beautiful garden, surrounded by lots of people in gorgeous clothes. In the middle of the crowd, there was a giant ball-shaped thing, with a large basket at the bottom.

Before I could even clean my feathers after the journey, I was lifted up and put into the basket. The sheep and the cockerel were already there.

"They're going to cook us!" moaned the sheep. "I can smell burning."

Just then there was a big cheer from the ground, and the basket shook. The cockerel started squawking and the sheep cowered on the bottom of the basket.

I jumped up to the rail of the basket and looked over the edge. We were in the air! Below us I could see the shocked faces of the crowd gazing upwards.

"We're flying!" I told the cockerel and the sheep.

"But sheep can't fly!" wailed the sheep. "It isn't natural!"

"Well, they can now," I told him. "You're the first flying sheep! Congratulations!"

The sheep stopped wailing and looked at me.

"Does that mean I'll be famous?" he asked.

"Oh yes!" I told him. "You'll be the most famous sheep ever!"

"Hurrah!" cried the sheep, and jumped up to look over the side of the balloon.

We were flying over the King's palace now, high above the treetops. We flew over the courtyard and I could see all the people waving and pointing.

Then suddenly the balloon juddered, and started to move downwards.

"Look out!" I called.

We hit the ground with a thump. For a moment I could hardly hear anything. And then came a sound like hundreds of tiny clicks. It was the sound of people clapping. Two hands picked me up, and I looked into the eyes of one of the men who came to the farm.

He carried me over to a red carpet where he bowed. In front of me was a man sitting on a chair in the shiniest clothes I had ever seen.

"Well done, Joseph Montgolfier," said the man. "And well done to the animals."

I don't know what all the fuss was about. Ducks have been flying for years.

This story quacks me up...

Make sure you read <u>every single word</u>, won't you.

Getting Off The Ground

Don't forget — information tells you a <u>load of facts</u>.
Take it nice and <u>slowly</u> so you've got time to soak them all up.

Introduction

Balloons can come in lots of different shapes and sizes.

Hot-air balloons

Hot-air balloons are mostly used for fun. Some people go on balloon trips to see the view from the sky. Other people have balloon races or try to fly long distances. Two men have even flown all the way around the world in a balloon!

Weather Balloons

Some balloons carry weather equipment into the atmosphere — they send back information about air temperature and pressure. Scientists track them to find out the speed of the wind.

Airships

Airships are special balloons driven by propellers. They are usually quite long and pointed, instead of being round. In the 1930s they were used to carry passengers around the world. Today you can still see some airships, but they are much less common.

Party balloons

Party balloons are small rubber bags. You blow air into them until they have stretched as far as they can go. Then you tie the end. The air can't escape, so the balloon stays inflated.

You can also get small helium balloons. They float in the air all the time — so if you take one outside make sure you hang on to the string or the balloon will float away into the sky!

Balloon Facts

- Hot-air balloons are like giant bags. A flame is used to heat the air inside. The hot air is lighter than the cold air, so the balloon floats in the sky. The pilots let the air in the balloon get cooler when they want to go down.

- In early hot-air balloons, the air was heated by burning straw. Today most balloons burn propane gas.

- Hot-air balloons were the first working aircraft invented by human beings. The first balloons were tested in 1782, and were made out of paper and linen. Today, most hot-air balloons are made out of nylon.

Keep going — you're <u>nearly there</u> now.

How a Hot-Air Balloon Works

The hot air inside the balloon is lighter than the cool air outside it, so the balloon floats up into the sky.

When the people in the balloon want to come down they turn off the flames.

The air in the balloon cools down, and the balloon sinks back to earth.

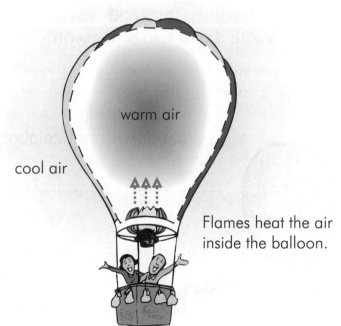

warm air

cool air

Flames heat the air inside the balloon.

It's all just a lot of hot air...

Well done! You've read <u>everything</u> now.

Poem Questions

The questions <u>start</u> here. They're in the <u>same order</u> as the bits of writing, so the first questions are on the <u>poem</u>.

Q: Answer these questions about the poem **"My Balloon"**. (page 39)

1 What kind of balloons is the poem about?

☐ hot-air balloons   ☐ party balloons

☐ pink balloons   ☐ weather balloons

Look back at the poem to find the answers — it's the only way to be <u>sure</u> you're getting them right.

2 Whose balloon sank into a bog?

....

3 The words 'tree' and 'sea' at the end of the first two lines **rhyme**. Write down two other words from the poem that rhyme.

....

4 What do you notice about how the **last verse** begins?

....

5 How does the word 'bang' stand out on the page?

....

Don't get bogged down...

Try and answer <u>all the questions</u>, even the tricky ones.

Story Questions

These questions are about the <u>story</u>, "The First Balloon Ride".
Don't start trying to <u>make up</u> the answers. Look at <u>what happens</u> in the story.

Q: Answer these questions about **"The First Balloon Ride"**. (pages 40 & 41)

1   What was the 'giant ball-shaped thing'?

    ....

2   Why did the sheep think the animals were going to be cooked?

    ....

3   How do you think the sheep felt when he **looked over the side** of the basket?

The answer <u>isn't</u> written in the story. You'll have to <u>think</u> about what the sheep <u>did</u> and <u>said</u>.

☐ excited   ☐ angry

☐ lost   ☐ confused

4   Who is telling the story?

    ....

5   Why do you think the man in shiny clothes said "Well done"?

    ....

That sheep's a bit of a basket case...

Some questions are hard, but they're <u>never</u> impossible.

Information Questions

Here are some more <u>lovely juicy questions</u> about balloons. They're about the information in "Getting Off the Ground". Use the <u>diagrams</u> as well as the <u>words</u>.

Q: Answer these questions about the information piece, **"Getting Off the Ground"**. (pages 42 & 43)

1   Name two things that weather balloons measure.

....

....

2   What is the shape of an airship like?

....

3   Why do you tie a knot in a party balloon?

....

4   Finish these sentences using the **Balloon Facts**.

The pilots let the air in the balloon

....

....

The first balloons

....

....

It's knot that hard...

Remember they could ask about the <u>pictures</u> too.

Questions on the Whole Lot

The last lot of questions asks you to think about <u>all the bits of writing</u>.

Q: Answer these questions.
They're about **all the pieces of writing** in this section.

1   On the chart tick (✓) the part of the book where you have read these things about balloons.

	My Balloon	The First Balloon Ride	Getting Off the Ground
Charlie's balloon lost all of its air.			
Most hot-air balloons are made of nylon.			
The cockerel squawked, and the sheep cowered.			
Airships were once used to carry passengers.			

2   Which piece of writing tells you **facts** about balloons?

☐ the Contents   ☐ Getting Off the Ground

☐ My Balloon   ☐ The First Balloon Ride

3   On which page can you find a diagram showing how a hot-air balloon works?

....

Don't get in a flap...

One last little thing — <u>check your answers</u>.

Section Five — Up and Away

Writing a Letter

<u>Don't</u> sit back and relax yet — <u>have a go</u> at this writing task.

The sheep in the story "The First Balloon Ride" was **scared** at first, but then he **enjoyed** the flight. Pretend you are the sheep, and **write a letter** to someone you know, telling them about your adventure.

Before you actually start writing you'll need some <u>ideas</u>.
<u>Answering these questions</u> first should give you <u>loads</u>.

Who is your letter to?

....

<u>Think about</u> the person you're going to write to, and what they'd like to know.

Write down **three things** that happened that you want to write about.

You <u>don't</u> have to talk about exactly the same things as the duck.

① ....

....

② ....

....

③ ....

....

Think about how you **felt**:

before you went up in the balloon

....

when you were in the air

....

when you were on the ground again

....

Writing about the sheep's <u>feelings</u> will make the letter sound <u>real</u>.

Remember you're <u>the first ever sheep</u> who's been up in a balloon.
The person you're writing to would be really interested in what things <u>looked like</u>.

Write down some **interesting words** you can use to describe what you saw when you were **on the ground**, and up **in the air**.

....

....

Now you're <u>ready to start</u> — so grab a piece of paper, and <u>scribble away</u>.

You're writing a letter, so make sure you do all these things too.

1) Put your <u>address</u> at the top of the page — you can use <u>yours</u> or <u>make one up</u>.

2) Put "<u>Dear</u>" and the <u>person's name</u>.

3) Sign off at the end, with something like "<u>Lots of love</u>" and the <u>sheep's name</u>.

<u>Yours sheepishly...</u>

Try and use <u>all these ideas</u> when you write your letter.

In at the Deep End

Writing a story <u>isn't</u> as easy as it looks. You need loads of <u>practice</u>.

Read the story on these two pages carefully.
Then <u>answer the questions</u> on pages 52 and 53.

In at the Deep End

"Can I go swimming, Mum?"
"But you don't like swimming, Pete," Mum said, confused.
"Everyone's going. Please!" I begged her.
"Alright then, but I'll make sure Jo keeps an eye on you."

My cousin Jo was the lifeguard at the swimming pool. She always kept an eye out for me. Mum drove me to the pool. "I'll be in the parents' section with the other mums," she said. "Tell your cousin to call me if you need me."

I went into the changing rooms and met Sam. He was the leader of our gang.
"You're late!" he said. "Get a move on." He went through to the pool.

I got changed and went through to the pool. The others were in the water already. I went towards the shallow end.

"Don't be such a scaredy cat!"
It was Sam again. He was always picking on me.
"Are you afraid of going into the deep end?" he asked.
"No," I told him, "I just don't want to."
"Coward!" he hissed.

"Hi there!" I looked around. It was Jo.
"Hi Jo," I said.
"I didn't think you liked swimming, Pete," Jo grinned.
Sam looked at me and laughed.
I felt my ears burning with embarrassment.
"I wanted to practise," I muttered.
"Good for you!" Jo smiled and walked away.
Straightaway Sam turned to me.

"Scaredy cat!" he laughed. "You can't swim! You're scared of the deep end!"
"Yes I can!" I shouted. I was furious with Sam for making fun of me.

I know this story <u>looks</u> really long and tricky but <u>don't worry</u> — take your time.

"Jump in the water then!" sneered Sam.

Without thinking I jumped. The water was deeper than I thought. I could feel it bubbling in my nose. It was horrible. I was really frightened. I tried to move my arms and legs but I couldn't. I was going to drown.

Then suddenly, my head was above the water. I was alright, I could breathe again. And then I realised — I was swimming! I could see all around the pool. I swam to the side, and saw Jo watching me from her chair. She waved at me.

The rest of the gang swam over. "Well done!" said Eric. "That was brilliant," said Lee. "Where's Sam?" I asked. No one knew. Then we saw him. He was up by the deep end.

"I'll show you how to swim," he shouted, and divebombed into the water. He disappeared in a great splash.
"Where's he gone?" I shouted. Suddenly he popped up like a cork, waving his hands in the air. "Help!" he screamed.

There was a quick splash from behind us and Jo swam past. She grabbed Sam under his arms and pulled him to the side. Everybody watching clapped.

Sam's mum came and took him home. The rest of us got out, but before we could go to get changed, Jo came up to us.

"Well done Pete!" she said to me.
"But you're the hero," I said. "You saved Sam."

"You were just as brave, " she told me. "You were scared of swimming but you still went into the pool." She patted me on the shoulder. I felt really happy.

"I'll see you in the pool next week," she said.
"Definitely," I replied.

It's sink or swim time...
<u>Read</u> the story and <u>turn over</u>. It's as easy as that.

Writing a Story

Stories can be pots of <u>fun</u> to write. Use this page to <u>help</u> you write one.

Read through the story 'In at the Deep End' again
and <u>answer the questions</u> about it on this page.

Who is the person **telling** the story?

....

What is the story **about**?

HINT: Think what happens at the <u>end</u>.

....

....

How does Pete **describe his feelings** so we can imagine them?

Write down <u>all</u> the words he uses to say what he feels.

....

....

....

Me? Scared?

Have a <u>quick think</u> about these questions too.

- What has Pete found out about swimming?
- How do you think he feels about swimming now?
- Does this story make you want to do something you're afraid of?
  What do you think it would be like?

'In at the Deep End' is a story about something that <u>really happened</u>.
Write <u>your own story</u> about something that really happened to you.

Write about a time when you did something you were **afraid of**.

A Scary Experience

These bits are here to help you <u>get some ideas</u> for your story.

Write down the thing you were afraid of.

....

It can be <u>anything</u> you want to write about,
like acting in a play maybe, or picking up a spider.

Think of **two things** that could happen in the story.

① ....

② ....

Write down some **interesting words** to describe **how you felt**.

....

....

<u>Don't forget</u> to think about these things as well.

- how to start and end your story
- how to organise your ideas

I feel great!

<u>Write your story</u> on a new piece of paper.

Hmmm, a likely story...

Come on — make your story nice and <u>interesting</u>.

The Ancient Egyptians

This is about a pretty amazing bunch of people — the Ancient Egyptians.

Read it carefully, and look at how the information is set out on the pages. Each different part of the writing has a subheading and pictures.

Ancient Egyptians

The Ancient Egyptian civilization lasted about 3000 years. It was most powerful around 4000 years ago. The Ancient Egyptians were ruled by a king called a **pharaoh**.

Pyramids

The **Pyramids** were built as tombs for dead pharaohs. The pharaohs had their treasure buried with them in the pyramids. The very first pyramid was built for the pharaoh Zoser. It is known as the Step Pyramid because of its shape.

The Step Pyramid of Zoser

The Great Pyramid.

The famous Pyramids at Giza were built around 2500 BC. The biggest pyramid is the pyramid of the pharaoh Khufu. Each side is 230 metres long, which is as long as two full-size football pitches. The pyramid is 138m high, which is about 70 times as high as a house.

The stone blocks used to build the pyramids are very heavy. The Ancient Egyptians didn't have any machines, so all the blocks had to be moved by hand. Most people think that the Egyptians put a ramp up the side of the pyramid. Large teams of men pulled the blocks up on rollers or on sledges.

In order to build such a huge structure, thousands of people must have been needed. No one is absolutely sure how many people worked on the pyramids, or exactly how they were built.

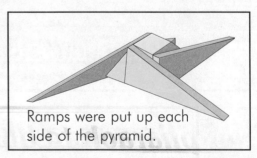

Ramps were put up each side of the pyramid.

Watch out for all the tricky new words in the article — try to learn them!

Egyptian art

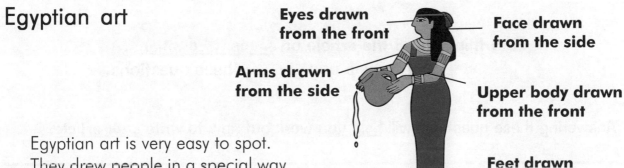

Eyes drawn
from the front

Face drawn
from the side

Arms drawn
from the side

Upper body drawn
from the front

Feet drawn
from the side

Egyptian art is very easy to spot.
They drew people in a special way
that wasn't exactly like real life.

Egyptian writing

Most people in Ancient Egypt couldn't read or write. People called **scribes** had the job of writing. They had been to school and had learnt to read and write. They wrote on bits of broken pottery, then rubbed the writing off when they were finished. When they needed to write something important, they used paper made from reeds. This paper was called **papyrus**.

Egyptians had two kinds of writing. The first kind was called **hieroglyphics**. Each letter of the alphabet was a picture. This meant that hieroglyphics took a long time to write. The Egyptians also had an everyday writing which was like a simpler version of hieroglyphics. It was much easier to write.

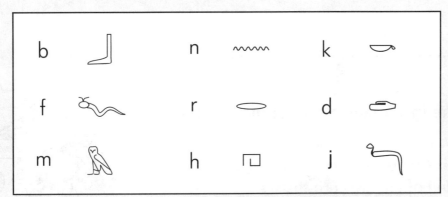

Examples of some hieroglyphic letters.

Not pharaoh to go, now...

Think about what sort of things make the writing interesting.

Writing Information

Yes — it's your <u>big chance</u> to <u>write an article</u> like the one you just read.

First think about the article on <u>Ancient Egyptians</u>.
<u>Look back</u> at it to help you <u>answer</u> these questions.

Answering these questions will <u>help you</u> work out <u>how</u> to write <u>your article</u>.

What are the **different parts** of the article about?

Don't forget — the article has got <u>three</u> main parts.

Part 1 ....

Part 2 ....

Part 3 ....

What have you found out about the Egyptians?

Think about the <u>kind</u> of thing you found out — like the <u>way they wrote</u>.

....

....

How is the information set out on the pages?

Look out for how the article's <u>divided up</u>.
What kind of <u>pictures</u> are there?

Bellies

Heads

Tails

....

....

Make a plan for <u>your own</u> piece of writing about a <u>different</u> group of people.

It needs to be in <u>your own words</u>,
but you can <u>find out</u> information from <u>anywhere</u> you like.

People from History

Choose **1 group** of people from history to write about.
Tick the one you choose.

Romans ☐   Victorians ☐   Vikings ☐   Your own idea ☐

Now think of <u>three parts</u> for your writing.

Write down what the **title** of each part will be.

① ....

② ....

③ ....

<u>Before</u> you start writing, think about these <u>important things</u>.

- how you will **set out** your writing.

  You could use <u>bullet points</u> and <u>subheadings</u> to keep things clear.
  Try drawing some <u>pictures</u> as well.

- how you will make it **interesting**.

  Try using plenty of <u>different</u> words.
  See if you can write sentences using words like '<u>because</u>' or '<u>so</u>'.

Get some paper and <u>write</u> your piece.
<u>Use your notes</u> to help you.

Brush up your skills...

Write <u>neatly</u>, and don't let it all get <u>boring</u>.

Section 1:   Writing Skills

Page 1   Capital Letters
Q1
✓, ✗, ✓, ✗
Q2
Answers should be filled in in this order — all capital letters
T, P, W, E, I, L, C, H

Page 2   Finishing Sentences
Q1
Nectar is a sweet liquid found in flowers. Butterflies and moths eat nectar. Their mouths are like long straws. They reach inside the flower and suck up all the nectar.
Q2
?, ., ?, !, ?, !, !, ., .

Page 3   Using Speech Marks
Q:
"Do you want to see my tarantula?" Gary asked.
Abdul said, "Shall I come round after school?"
Gary replied, "No need, I've got it here."
"What did you say?" gasped the bus driver.
"Don't worry, it's not very big," Gary said cheerfully.

Pages 4-5:   Paragraphs
Q1
a) 5, b) 4, c) 3, d) 5
Q2
person — Ginger, person — Larry, place — jungle
Q3
Any suitable continuation. Paragraph should have indent on first line.

Pages 6-7   Writing a Story
Q1
① The giant snail was always hungry.
   She ate all the food in the fields.

③ While I was helping the elephants sang me a
   song. They asked me to come back next week.
Or any suitable ending.

② Inside, she found the most amazing fruits.
   She ate one then went to see what was upstairs.
Or any suitable middle.
Q2

happy   worried   amused

angry   grumpy   scared

   Or any other suitable answers.
Q3
cycled, bought, shouted, climbed, took
Or any other suitable answers.

Page 8   Writing a Letter
Q1
Address of the child doing the question; today's date; any suitable name for the person the letter is written to; child's own name to sign off.

Q2
Lots of love, Best wishes, All the best

Page 9   Writing Information
Q:
               Frog Spawn
•   Clear balls of jelly.
•   You see it in the spring.
•   It's really hundreds of frogs' eggs.
•   Each black speck grows into a tadpole.
Or any other suitable answers.

Section 2:   Reading Comprehension

Page 11   What You Have to Do
Q1
The electrical speech machine.
Q2
To hold the cables up in the air.
Q3
they can carry more information

Pages 12-13 Stories
Q1
Because Charlie couldn't see anything.
Q2
fairies
Q3
a bowl of fruit and nuts
Q4
3, 2, 1, 4

Pages 14-15 Information Writing
Q1
things preserved in rock.
Q2
It rots away.
Q3
Brachiosaurus
Q4
46m, *or* The same length as five buses parked end to end
Q5
It was about the same weight.

Page 17   Poems
Q1
the robin
Q2
happy
Q3
year — clear, spring — sing, bad — sad, wings — sings, there — Air
Q4
that he is a friend

Section 3:   All About Food

Page 18   Getting Started
Q1
page 6
Q2
The Lizard and the Peach

Page 19   Salad
Q1
2 of the following: lettuce, celery, cucumber, tomato
Q2
great

Pages 20-21 The Lizard and the Peach
Q1
flies
Q2
because the peach would be nicer than flies
Q3
3 of the following: sweet, soft, juicy, delicious, fresh
Q4
by jumping
Q5
He says the peach is rotten because he's cross he can't get it.
Or any other suitable answers.

Page 22   What's on the Menu
Q1
In the UK, half a million curries are eaten every day. The most popular takeaway meal in Britain is fish and chips.
Q2
Glasgow
Q3
mushroom, ham and pepperoni

Page 23   Questions on the Whole Lot
Q1

	Salad	The Lizard and the Peach	What's on The Menu?
Most people eat fish and chips at least once a month.			✓
It was time for action.		✓	
Give me celery, it tastes great!	✓		
His belly made a slapping sound when it hit the ground.		✓	

Q2
They're both bored of their normal food.
Q3
The Lizard and the Peach

Pages 24-25 Writing a Story
The plan should make sense. The final story should follow the plan.

Section 4:   Frost and Snow

Pages 28-29 A Wintry Weekend
Q1
The rain on his windows, and the dog barking.
Q2
cold raindrops
Q3
Because the wind was blowing the rain sideways — he was using his umbrella to protect himself.
Q4
the rain was sticking her fur down

Q5
They were covered in snow.
Q6
wearing thick white gloves
Q7
Chris and Candy are happy
Q8
1) Chris got up
2) Chris took Candy for a walk
3) They get home
or Chris says something about the day

Page 30-31   Snow Facts
Q1
ice crystals
Q2
Bratsk, in Siberia
Q3
...Canada and the northern United States, than at the North Pole.
...if they don't melt before they get there.
or
...if the air is freezing all the way down from the cloud.
Q4
Because the air is warmer at the the bottom — the snowflakes melt before they get there.
Q5
wet snow

Page 33   Frosty Stories
Q1
It freezes in a beautiful pattern that looks like flowers.
Q2
with her kisses
Q3
He gives her fur coats and jewels.
Q4
a person causes the cold weather

Page 34   Questions on the Whole Lot
Q1
A Wintry Weekend
Q2
Frosty Stories
Q3
...it was wearing a thick white glove.
...and turns their hearts to ice with her deadly kisses.

Page 35   Writing Information
What have you found out?
Any facts about snowflakes from the article.

How is the information set out?
using a heading, using bullet points

Pages 36-37 Writing Information
The plan should make sense. The final piece should follow the plan.

Section 5:   Up and Away

Page 44   Poem Questions
Q1
party balloons
Q2
Sarah's
Q3
dog—bog, air—hair, drain—train *or* light—tight
Q4
It talks about the writer's own balloon — the others all start by talking about other people's balloons.
Q5
BANG is in capital letters, has an exclamation mark after it, *or* has a whole line to itself.

Page 45   Story Questions
Q1
A hot air balloon.
Q2
Because it could smell burning.
Q3
excited
Q4
the duck
Q5
Because the balloon flight was successful.
Or any suitable answer.

Page 46   Information Questions
Q1
2 of the following:
air temperature, air pressure, wind speed
Q2
They are quite long and pointed.
Q3
So the air doesn't escape.
Q4
The pilots let the air in the balloon get cooler when they want to go down.

The first balloons were tested in 1782 *or* were made out of paper and linen.

Page 47   Questions on the Whole Lot
Q1

	My Balloon	The First Balloon Ride	Getting Off the Ground
Charlie's balloon lost all of its air.	✓		
Most hot-air balloons are made of nylon.			✓
The cockerel squawked, and the sheep cowered.		✓	
Airships were once used to carry passengers.			✓

Q2
Getting Off The Ground
Q3
page 43

Pages 48-49 Writing a Letter
The plan should make sense. The final letter should follow the plan.

Section 6:   In at the Deep End

Page 52   Writing a Story
Who tells the story:
Pete *or* a boy

What the story's about:
A boy who learns not to be scared of swimming.

How Pete describes his feelings:
'felt his ears burning with embarrassment', 'furious', 'horrible', 'really frightened', 'felt really happy'

Page 53
The plan should make sense. The final story should follow the plan.

Section 7:   The Ancient Egyptians

Page 56   Writing Information
The different parts:
Part 1: Pyramids
Part 2: Egyptian art
Part 3: Egyptian writing

What have you found out?
Any facts about Egyptians from the article.

How is the information set out?
subheadings, paragaphs, pictures, diagrams, labels
(or any other suitable comments)

Page 57
The plan should make sense. The final piece should follow the plan.

Well, looks like you've finished.